The Transformative Power of Tattoo

short stories & poetry

Edited by Julianne Ingles

guts publishing

"Wear your heart on your skin in this life."
— Sylvia Plath

Editor's Note

I always seem to be looking for an answer, or answers, in our anthologies. I don't really think I would put one together unless there was some compelling reason.

But in this one I didn't exactly know what I was looking for. The idea of a tattoo anthology started to percolate in 2022 when I had a client who was a tattooist. As you might suspect she's well-tattooed, and when I first met her I immediately noticed the vines and leaves on her upper chest and neck that climbed all the way up to her chin. When we first started having our Zoom meetings I was fascinated by her look. It seemed to make her other-worldly.

At one point I posted a photo of her on social media, which got a lot of attention. And that's when Liam Hogan – our 4x anthology contributor and off-the-charts short story writer – sent a message to me to say: *Why don't you do a tattoo anthology?*

Shortly after that I posted an open call for short story and poetry submissions and they started pouring in. Liam's was first, of course, and it did land in this anthology. A short story called 'Chiaroscuro' that is somewhere in the scifi-ish genre.

My assistant Amandine did the first round of reading. Then Pina, a friend who runs the GLITS events at Goldsmiths, joined in. It was a long process. Anthologies always are because you are dealing with so many different genres and I never want to be limited by my own personal tastes. So, first of all, I am immensely grateful to Amandine and Pina for their input and expertise. Thank you both. It literally took us months.

In the end we selected 6 essays, 6 short stories and 7 poems. And although that was really a challenge, it wasn't nearly as challenging as trying to figure out the common thread. I started wishing I'd been more specific in the call for submissions, like My First Tattoo, or Tattooist Tattoo Stories, or anything other than just tattoos.

But when I got into reading really carefully and intuitively, I started to see the thread was transformation. Even with all of the different genres and tones and personalities, that was the primary theme. When someone got a tattoo, something happened. Small or large. A shift occurred psychologically when their physical appearance was altered.

I should also mention that my client who inspired the anthology, Erin Hosfield, also landed in this anthology with an essay titled: 'What's the weirdest thing you ever tattooed?' She is the only contributor who, to the best of my knowledge, is actually a tattooist. And it is also the one exception where the transformation theme doesn't entirely apply. Her essay is more about how she is sometimes viewed as a magical entity with special powers, which I guess does fit in with transformation to an extent, and also a number of interesting observations about people's ideas about what kind of images to tattoo and on what part of their body. It is a fascinating look at the psychology of tattooing, which in time became my primary question: Why do people do it?

I say that because I have no real experience with tattoos aside from looking at them. When I first moved to London in 2010 I noticed how common they were and I suspect the likes of Amy Winehouse propelled the tattooing trend even further into the stratosphere. By 2023, I think it's safe enough to say that tattooing is fairly mainstream, or at the very least, a somewhat acceptable practice which in the recent past (in the West) was considered class-related and taboo with loads of stereotypes attached.

In May of 2023, I went to the Great British Tattoo Show in London. It was the most bizarre and wonderful experience. I went mostly to do field research and I know that may sound funny, but it's true. I walked into an auditorium-sized room, which is the grand ballroom at Alexandra Palace with vaulted ceilings and polished marble floors, to be met by the buzz of tattoo guns and kiosk after kiosk of tattooists with clients on tattooing tables (not too different from a dental chair), definitely having some kind of experience. It seemed somewhat sacred. I watched as the guns pushed ink under the skin, and as the tattooist wiped away blood and leaking ink, and then I got brave and started to talk to people and say: *Do you mind if I ask why you're getting a tattoo?*

The answers were fascinating. Most people said because they liked the way it looked. Period. And I was like, really? And they were like, yes. But I felt that I needed to go deeper so I started asking about transformation, and if their tattoo was symbolic or somehow meaningful. Almost all said, yes, it was about that on the first one but after that it became a way to enhance their body or the way they perceived their body, which was eye-opening for me: Tattoos made them feel better about themselves. I then decided that this did actually fit with my idea of the theme of transformation. Although it's important to mention that some of them also said that it became something like an addiction – the buzz and high of getting a new tattoo and looking at it and feeling their body had been transformed (not to mention the actual painful process itself) only lasted a certain amount of time. Then they had to get another one.

So, I think it's safe enough to say there are many different reasons people get tattoos, but in the end they are somewhat magical or transformational. I say 'or' because magical implies something positive, and transformational not as much, and I don't want to imply this collection is all warm and fuzzy. There are a few that tackle the darker side of tattooing which I feel is important in terms of balance.

I would like to thank all of our contributors. I am delighted and honoured that your work is part of this collection. It represents years, and lifetimes, of honing your craft and constantly improving your skills. And you all make it look so effortless. Thank you.

Dear reader, I hope you enjoy this collection. Although each piece feels wildly different from the next, I have done my best to create flow in the way they are sequenced and also with my own comments interspersed to guide you through in a meaningful way.

As always, thank you for your support of Guts Publishing.

Julianne Ingles
27 August 2023
Director at Guts

Contents

The Transformative Power of Tattoo

Ready?
Here we go.

First,
on why
they
do
it.

Daniela Esposito
Mayflies in Winter

The first was a light bulb, a nineteenth century light bulb drawn by a man named L — he played only heavy metal, and his eyeballs were no longer white. It will be several months before my next. I'm lying in the hotel room. It is a ground floor room in a Premier Inn by a motorway and the man I split the hotel cost with has already left and, except for three hairs of stubble in the sink, there is no trace of him even being here. I met him at a party after my friends had gone home. He gave me a tab of ecstasy and we both declared our love for one another, which was true when we said it, but not anymore. Most of my feelings are like this, existing in narrow time-frames with the lifespan of a mayfly or other such insect that perishes after a matter of hours.

Rising from the bed, I need to let some air out, I say in my head as if I am an overfilled balloon. There is nothing sharp in the room. Nothing. I search for a pen, the kind that slides neatly onto ties and clipboards like the one sitting on the desk beside a greeting card signed by Julie telling me to have a nice visit because I should just know who Julie is, like God or Beyonce. Also on the desk is a still-warm cookie establishing a puddle of grease that offers a window into the paper bag, in this case, an idle chocolate chip. It must have been delivered by Julie whilst I was sleeping, or from the man with whom I shared the bed.

From a distance (the bed to the desk), it looks like a real fountain pen, but close-up it is only imitating a fountain pen, and has very little of the anatomy of a fountain pen. For one, it does not have that sharper than sharp nib that would just have done the trick. What it does have is a metal clip. Except this one is not pointed but rounded off and impotent. I tear open a little pot of milk. What am I thinking? So I sip the tepid milk and throw the plastic into the bin. And then I find a bottle of carbonated water in the mini fridge. The lid is serrated, only slightly, but it could just do the trick. And then I pay £2.69 just to 'let a little air out' as fifties housewives might 'take the edge off' with a tipple or two of sherry.

A jagged line of blood forms, obedient and uniform like a relay of sprinters' feet; a sequence of droplets dark as beetle juice and imperceptibly connected by the serrated edge. And then I place my arm under the sink and watch the blood wash away beneath the stream of water, before wrapping it in one of the nice flannels warmed up by the radiated handrail. And I wonder if the towels are all new or just washed each time and how they get them to look as new as that. Feeling accomplished, I climb into bed, strait-jacketing myself between the crisp sheets as I watch some *Deal or No Deal* and *A Place in the Sun*, the sort of daytime television which I feel I only have licence to watch in hotel rooms, alone. If anyone asks (about the scratch on my arm) I will say I got caught in a bramble, somewhere.

I'm packing up my stuff, moving slowly so that I don't have to confront the harsh white sunshine and the journey home. I follow a man named S on Instagram. He posts a story advertising an opening that afternoon at 2:15pm. I DM him to say I'll be there, before sending a deposit over PayPal. And just like that, I'm on my way, my hangover repurposed, and when I get off the train, I run into Superdrug to buy a disposable razor and some deo and then I shave my arm-pits in the toilet of Pret and freshen up and soon I'm lying on a couch in a dank room that smells pungently of bleach. Several heads, many of them shaved and tattooed, loom over arms and legs, backsides and scalps, and except for the rumbling of machines, there is a silence that hinges on sacred.

He pings the gloves on and wheels himself over to me so that I can smell his sweat, but it's not bad. I tell him I'll take whatever, and wherever. I ask him what he thinks as I let my arms go limp, as I suck in my belly and push out my chest. Permitting his eyes to survey me like the days' catch, his gaze falls somewhere between that of a doctor and a lover. He stops decidedly at my inner arm. I don't know what he sees in that piece of unnamed flesh, but he's pressing a stencil onto the skin and soon he warns me that

9

he is beginning now. I don't look during the procedure, instead asking questions about him because I want to be special to the man whose stains will remain with me forever. Sometimes there is a silence that isn't uncomfortable, and my mind drifts off, thoughts floating past unhatched.

All done, he says, peeling off the rubber and wheeling himself away to clean up. I must have drifted off, both lulled and fortified by the rhythm of pain. I look down to find a naked lady on my inner arm, reading a book by an open window. When I bend my elbow, I can sit her up or recline her. I can make her thinner or fatter. I can open her book or close it (though I don't know what she is reading, but I decide that it is something by Simone de Beauvoir. I will eventually settle on *The Mandarins*). He nods, as he rinses my blood off in the sink.

Yes, she was a life-sitter, he says. *We were together for a few years. Oh,* I say, trying to conceal my surprise and envy which swarms to my cheeks explosively and without warning, but he's not looking. I wonder if they got together before or after she sat for him. *We have a child together. Christ, he must be five years old now,* he ponders, squinting at the overhead light. As if even synthetic light could illuminate his past, could colour his son's cheeks, his button nose, could — bring him to life.

And when I look down, I notice that wrapped up in the blanket by the woman's feet is a small child. S, whose name I realise I do not know, and now do not wish to, is continuing to wash his hands of me, leaving me on the couch with my bloody lady and her bastard baby. He turns to face me now, and noticing my exposed arm, he clamours to reach for the roll of plastic film, his movements suddenly oafish and brusque. He wraps me up several times over so that my arm bursts beneath the plastic like a shank of ham.

Was the window really open? I ask. It is the first time he's really looked at me all afternoon, his mouth twisting into an almost smile. *Why do you ask? Because outside the trees are rakish and bare. It must have been winter. Huh. Good observation.* But he's already turned to another matter and so I sit up, the paper towel resilient beneath me. A little dizzy, as if I myself have just given birth, I stumble from the room with a young mother and child to look after.

There are many after — a masked skull, a pot of pansies, a fish bone, the face of my favourite childhood actor. And then the hankering returns. It is winter, but I'm not unhappy. I work in Paperchase selling stationary for the Christmas run and I'm off to start my masters the following January. The trees outside resemble those outside the window where my lady sits quietly reading. Here, few can see her, only those taking my blood or people I sleep with, and even then I tell them that she's just a life-sitter, no one special! I see a sign that says walk-ins welcome. My visits here have acquired the routineness of getting a tooth pulled, or a mole removed, or some other minor surgical procedure that might be deemed necessary. Here, I'm to let a stranger score his marks into a piece of my flesh, often a part without a name, that softer than soft patch on the inner elbow, for example. There is something substantiating about it, as if through a cherub's face or a daffodil's head, I am now existing for the first time. I realise it is just as much about having them on me as it is about giving a slice of myself to strangers at various stations throughout the country.

What would you like? he asks. For once, I am decisive. I stand up straight. *I would like a mayfly,* I declare. *Yes, I'd like a mayfly and I would like it right here.* Afterwards, he wraps her up and the blood wriggles and writhes beneath the plastic. And forty-eight hours later, I peel away the film to find that she has not flown away or perished, but that she is right here where I left her.

I
clearly
remember
the day
I started hating
my body:
I was eleven.

Claire Askew
The needle: on being female and tattooed

[Trigger warning: this essay makes passing references to weight, being weighed, disordered eating, and body image.]

It's 10am on a gorgeous April morning in Edinburgh. I'm in Tollcross, stepping off a bus. Everyone who's going to work today has already gone, so it's quiet: the sun's falling in big white blades down the tenement fronts. I stop somewhere for a carryout cup of tea — it's handed to me black and stewed – and palm a couple of Ibuprofen. I'm fizzing with giddy adrenalin. I'm on my way to get tattooed.

I have a tattooist the way most people have a dentist, doctor, tax advisor. Jim is his name, and in his cuffed jeans, thick specs and long-sleeved wool sweater, he could be a hip high school teacher. I'm booked into his opening slot of the day: the first of two sittings for a half-sleeve, a tattoo that will cover the whole of my upper left arm. I've emailed a scrawly design for Jim — who knows that I cannot draw — to translate into something that will both fit in the space, and look great. I feel lucky to have found a tattooist I can do this with: someone who picks up what I'm putting down, however vague it might be. I've been to others — including three of Jim's colleagues at Edinburgh's Red Hot & Blue Tattoo — but he's my guy now. I can't imagine going to anyone else.

I lay the blame for my tattoo obsession at the feet of Melanie C. Like any girl who turned twelve in 1998, I loved the Spice Girls more than just about anything, and travelled all the way to Sheffield from my home in the Scottish Borders to see them live. But although I had my mum sew me a copy of Geri Halliwell's union jack dress, Mel C was always my favourite of the five, and it was her singing part I memorised from every song. More importantly, Mel C was the first tattooed woman I had ever seen. Before her, I'd been led to believe that tattoos were for sailors, bikers, or prisoners — and always for men.

When I arrive at Red Hot & Blue, I'm greeted by Gina, the receptionist. She hands me the standard, Xeroxed release form, which asks if I've eaten in the last two hours, if I have any serious medical conditions, if I'm prone to fainting. Gina's not the most heavily-tattooed woman I've seen, but she's close: her ink is impressive, and beautiful. I'd guess she's younger than me, and that might account for the fleeting sense of worry I feel as I look at the tattoos on her neck, the heels of her hands, her stretched lobes. *What if you need to get a different job someday?,* I catch myself thinking.

Of course, I'm a hypocrite: this is a question I bristle at whenever it's fielded to me. However, I know that many Britons still flinch at the sight of a tattooed individual, and that distaste for tattoos can translate into prejudice. In July of 2014, *The Guardian* ran a poll entitled: "Are tattoos unprofessional?" There were hundreds of responses, with 54% of people deciding that *yes, they are.* The comment thread garnered over 400 replies. One man's comment, "They say that people with tattoos aren't the brightest," was upvoted nearly 200 times. Another wrote, "If someone reveals a tattoo, my respect-o-meter absolutely plummets," and elsewhere, a man claiming to be a CEO wrote that visible tattoos "would be a deal breaker in the hiring process."

Many people — not all of them tattooed — fail to see how, for example, a classic swallow inked on the arm of a surgeon might in any way prevent him from doing his job. For me, being tattooed is no less professional than, say, rocking fancy earrings, or going make-up free, which are also things I choose to do with my appearance. I usually answer the *different job* question by saying I'd rather not work for any employer who cannot accept who I am — which is true, but of course I'm also being blasé. I *do* worry — and not just about how talented, well-rounded people like Gina might come to be unemployed in future years. I worry over the subtext of a comment like the "respect-o-meter" man's. How much of our prejudice against tattoos is mixed up with class? (Angelina Jolie's are *classy* — Cheryl Cole's are *tacky trash*.) Or gender? I am repeatedly asked how I'll feel when my tattoos "start to sag" — a question with sexist connotations that are barely veiled. I notice it's Gina I worry for, and never Jim — though under his V-neck he's inked in every visible space.

Anyway: as much as I value the respect of men who try and set the world to rights in online comment threads — here I am. I chat briefly with Jim about the foot-long, multi-coloured design, before giving him the OK to get the ball rolling. At this point he lays a transfer of the tattoo on my skin: it prints a temporary version of the linework on my arm in wet, purple ink. If I don't like the placement — a little higher, lower, bigger, smaller — this ghost tattoo can be easily wiped, re-printed, and pressed on again. I let Jim mess with it a bit until I like it. Now he can begin assembling his machine.

I clearly remember the day I started hating my body: I was eleven. At my tiny Scottish village primary school, there was no nurse — in my year group there were only six kids, so it wouldn't have been worth it. Instead, a peripatetic doctor travelled round the area's rural schools. The day came for primary sixes to get their health check, which included being weighed by this relative stranger. I tipped the scales at exactly ten stone: edging dangerously close to the wrong end of the optimal weight range. The doctor made it clear that I was big for my age — looking back, he meant *tall*, as I was already nearly five feet eight. But in my head, he meant I was a whale. I'd failed everyone: I was the one thing girls were not supposed to be. I was fat.

Of course, I was not fat. I look back now at photos of myself and at ten, at twelve, at seventeen, I was positively lanky. I only stopped growing when I hit five feet eleven inches tall, and my nickname in the first year of high school was *beanpole*. But by then, I'd lost control of my body image: the me I saw in my head was fat, ugly, and vile. I put myself on the same crash diets my mother had flirted with when I was a child: cabbage soup and workout videos with the curtains closed. Self-hatred breeds and thickens, and at twenty I was still behind its gauzy wall. I didn't have any recognised eating disorder, but I lived in the midst of what feminist critic Jean Kilbourne calls *disordered eating.* I even tried a diet where on Thursdays, I ate nothing but bananas and a pint of milk. Kilbourne reckons I wasn't alone: disordered eating affects around 4 in 5 women.

Jim's tattoo machine looks complex, so I've never asked about the tech. There are dials that he fiddles with every so often, and the whole thing's foot-pedal operated, like a sewing machine. I'm still surprised, even now, by the massive sound the contraption makes: always louder than I remember. Getting tattooed on the chest was especially startling, the gun and its rattling needle held inches from my face.

For a first tattoo, a chest-piece was an odd choice. The desire to have it done leapt up suddenly, though I'd been sketching out tattoo designs since Melanie C. One that came up again and again was a face inside a flower, an image nicked from an Alan Aldridge painting, then fiddled with. I scribbled it into the page of a notebook in a sunny square in Victoria, Canada, and two hours later, it was printed, twice — a perfect mirror image — on my collarbones. I was twenty-two, enjoying my first ever holiday abroad. My then-boyfriend, Leon — who was taken to his first tattoo appointment by his mum, days after he turned sixteen — was booked in with Gerry Kramer of Victoria's Tattoo Zoo. I jumped on his bandwagon, and landed hard.

People want to know about the pain. Back then, I did too. I'd had people tell me it felt like an elongated bee-sting; others had dug their fingernails into my arm, or pinched me, saying, "It's like this." In fact, it's different for everyone, and very much depends on *where*. I barely felt the ampersand being inked on the back of my neck, but some of the lines in the text on my feet made me wince. When I had a Hand of Protection put on my inner arm, the artist — Jim's colleague Alec Benjamin — said, "This spot might be a little sore." It wasn't too bad, but it's also a smallish tattoo. Being under the needle an hour is a very different thing to being under four.

It happened slowly: not after the chest-piece, or after the black-and-white linework of a swallow on my lower left leg. Not after the ampersand on my nape — a tattoo which, to this day, I've never seen. It might have started with the sexy mermaid, her turquoise tail and violet hair — my first colour piece, put on me by Hilary Dawson of the all-female Vancouver parlour Electro Ladylux. But I think it was the Hand of Protection, located on my upper arm: a site on the landscape of my body that I'd always loathed. Posting a photo of the finished tattoo on Facebook, I wrote, "New theory. Want to make a part of you more awesome? Put a tattoo on it." I was being flippant in that moment, but something had clicked. At the age of twenty-six, I was wresting control of my body image at last.

Jim has been tattooing for sixteen years. He's always ready with a welcome and some good craic, nagging Gina to bring his latest customer a cup of tea. You can tell he enjoys making people laugh. At every appointment he asks me whether I've Netflixed the bad Burt Reynolds films he waxes lyrical about. As I sit, the purple stencil drying on my arm, he switches out the stereo's death metal for some Bobby Darin, and declares a sing-along. Soon the whole room is busting out 'Lazy River' — Gina, me, the punters, artists — our bad karaoke carrying over the squashed-wasp sound of the machines. I like it that Jim doesn't patronise me: a tattoo parlour is still a pretty macho place, and I'm a woman who makes less-than-hip choices when it comes to her ink. Tattooing's a strangely intimate thing: you have to *like* the guy whose face is inches from your flesh. Or it helps, at least.

The first thing I do after every session — after I've powered home, burning adrenalin — is call my mum. She makes the same offended noise each time, but it's become a kind of family joke: *My daughter looks like a navvy!*, she tells her friends. But my mother knows, the way most women do, the importance of maintaining agency over the precious baggage of your female body. She likes that I wear t-shirts now, and I can recognise my own good likeness in a photograph.

"Your auntie's considering getting one," she tells me — she means her younger sister, Jude, who's in her sixties. "I've started a movement," I say, and hope it's true. In a world where — Kilbourne says — the female body is constantly airbrushed and whitened, made flat, a little illustration goes a long way.

What *is it* about tattooing, in the end? My favourite thing. It might be the smell: as I walk in the parlour this morning, the good, sterile *green* of it comes over me like a clean wind. It might be the wipe-down: a second of calm in the middle, where Jim changes inks, or needs to stretch, and the half-done tattoo is daubed before he starts again. The moment the clingfilm and tape comes off is special — and the first day you no longer itch, and know that it's healed.

It might be hearing the story that comes out of saying to a stranger, "That's a great tattoo." They all commemorate something: every tribal, every sparkly butterfly.

Jim says, "Alright — you comfy?" I nod, and the needle goes in.

Poetry next.
An
act
of
rebellion.

Di Lebowitz
Subversion

it started as an act of
    REBELLION
defiant
    SUBVERSION
of the cultural expectations a girl —
    A GOOD GIRL
chubby little mixed-race girl
with the Chinese mother from colonial Hong Kong
trapped in Paris
pretending at sixteen
to savour the exquisite *doleur*
the metallic smell of
    BLOOD
and
    INK
the sharp drill of an artist's needle
    SCRATCHING
out of flesh and ink I will fashion for
    MYSELF
a body — my body
one I can carve and claim as my
    OWN
later with a phoenix
then a dragon
and then waves

and bauhinias
and then calligraphy
in my mother's tongue:

  加油, 香港

  Add oil, Hong Kong

etchings to cover my body
to conceal the many marks left on me
etchings to fill in the cracks
too many to count now
broken and refilled
broken and repaired
paintings on my skin marking the passage of time
of

  HEALING

  BECOMING

  FINDING

an armour, a person-suit to face
a world not ready for women like

  ME.

I asked Liz Beth Turner to share some of the background on her poem FU. Here's what she said:

"Growing up, tattoos, alongside piercings and brightly coloured hair were absolutely anathema. The reasons were many and varied: I would be rejected by polite society; if I ever got arrested, I would be easily identifiable by the authorities; no-one would ever hire me; it would signify emotional instability and arrested development; I would be perceived as a n'er-do-well, a reprobate, a criminal; I should not disrespect my body in this way; it would attract the wrong kind of associates; I could die of blood poisoning; I could be stuck with a permanent mistake; I could be stuck with a reminder of someone I may not wish to remember later in life; I will look ridiculous as an old lady with misshapen tattoos on my sagging skin; I won't be taken seriously covered in sentimental claptrap. I could probably keep adding to this list of introjects and conditions of worth that shaped my own distorted beliefs about tattoos for many years."

Liz Beth Turner
FU

Absolutely not! Not as long as I
live and breathe! The end of my tattoo dream.

Instead I request a fountain pen; I
sell her a line about fine writing. She

buys it. And the ink. Next, the compass
conscripted from my geometry set.

Nervous but purposeful, set on self-
expression, I scratch at the layers of my

baby-thin skin with the sharp implement,
lightly at first, then with increased urgency.

What do I express though? I don't know so
I carve letters, deep into my thigh, then

force dark ink down in the wound with the pen.
She can't snoop there, but I'll know: my sly *FU.*

Later, when she no longer lives and breathes,
I ask a tattooist to cover it up with

a rose-entwined heart and a banner that says
MUM in fancy letters.

In Valerie Bence's bio she says:

Rembrandt is her muse and the subject of her first
collection *Falling in Love with a Dead Man.*

(Ok, now you can read her poem.)

Valerie Bence
Tatu – to puncture, to mark, to strike

THEN
 like this jagged shark-tooth pattern made zigzag
with a shark's tooth or chisel, soon enough the time comes
for '*striking the black*'; much preparation is needed

 to keep the tuhuna* supplied with inky pigment
in the tattoo house; *build a special fire pit to collect soot
from burned candlenuts, mix with coconut milk or gall*

 of shellfish, caught at night for the deepest black.
He lines up tools on tapa cloth, imbued with his personal
deities to limit pain and transfer mana** in the marks;

 flat instruments for straight lines, fine-work
or infill, gradual curved combs for cloud circles or wrapping
marks. Each tuhuna has a preferred comb material;

 serrated teeth, tortoiseshell, ray-spikes,
lemon thorns, bird or human bone; best of all is wing-bone
of albatross or elbow of frigate bird.

 Sharp pointed teeth are cut in the comb's edge
for tapping into skin to free the blood. An apprentice outlines
chosen marks in charcoal or coloured earth.

So it begins. With the biting comb
and a piece of tapa to wipe as he works, he dips
the comb quickly into ink and with each

swift tap of the mallet chants - *It is struck,*
it is struck, We tap yes, We tap you a little yes?
A painful rhythm, one hundred times a minute

for weeks; months before skin, covered
in scarification and blinking cicatrix shows the beauty
of the marks. This is powerful work

calling on ancestors for courage, to make each
session long, the days rest between are called the days of
blood. Some will die.

NOW

If I were there I would have lima (the hand tattoo)
for the honour to serve kava juice – but I am here
with you in this clean room, opting out of numbing
cream,
alcohol rubbed on my arm, cut stencil applied.
The machine begins its work buzzing like a thousand
bees,
its steady current drives sterile needles in and out of my skin
dermis deep, to fix the image.
As for ink, you say the best is from Japan
it could be Kuro Sumi or Dragon's Blood.

It is done.
I leave, with a man's face on my arm
wrapped in cling film…
It is an intoxication, a quiet curation.

* tattoo master
** a person, place or object's supernatural force

Nonfiction:
on living fearlessly,
fully
and
ferociously.

Emily Ricard
Indelibly Me

I distinctly remember the feeling of the marker gliding against the thin skin of my wrist; the smell of the ink, slightly acrid and wholly addictive causing me to scrunch up my nose as I inhaled. The black lines may not have been as crisp as I would have liked, gaining minute branches as they bled into the natural texture of my epidermis. I focused harder, doing my best to detail the feathers in the sparrow's wings before moving on to the rose. There was only half an hour of lunch break left and I was determined to finish my masterpiece before biology class.

"Such a freak," I heard someone jeer as they walked past me, giggles in their wake. I ignored them and kept drawing. I was used to the comments: I suppose dressing all in black, sporting nose rings and using myself as a life-size sketchpad made me stand out in the sea of popped collars, Ralph Lauren knits and artfully faded jeans. But I grew not to care. Even if I dressed like them, I would never fit in. I knew that because I began secondary school desperate to be accepted, confining my love of alternative style and rock solely to music, artfully concealing my true self under Dream Matte Mousse foundation, preppy clothes and Diesel jeans. Not anymore.

I focused hard on the rose. The curvature of the petals. The slightly unfurled centre. The subtle droop of the leaves. The chatter around me faded into nothingness, merely a hum, as I carefully finished the outline and picked up my fire engine red marker to colour it in. Out of nowhere, the shrill school bell rang out three times, causing me to jump and lose control of the pen. In dismay, I realised that the nib had bounced out of the linework and stopped just short of the anchor I had lovingly designed during history class. I sighed heavily and packed up my pencil case, throwing it in my canvas messenger bag. I'd have to find a way to fix it: spit and scrub or some ingenious redesigning. It wouldn't be my first cover-up.

* * *

"But why do you need to get a tattoo?" he asked, aimlessly flicking through the channels. It was a cold Monday night in London and the gas fire was whistling as I poured out two mugs of fragrant peppermint tea.

"You know I've always wanted one. Besides, I couldn't think of a more important tattoo to get than this one." I put our mugs down on two ceramic coasters and ensconced myself in a corner of the couch. I knew my father would never understand where I was coming from, my need to memorialise this terrifying and magnificent event in my skin. It had been almost two years since I fell ill and he still treated me with kid gloves, even though I'd been approved to come off blood thinners and my physical health was finally back on track. I knew it came from his love for me, but I couldn't help the frustration I was feeling at his obtuse remarks.

* * *

I often feel that I died and came back to life when I was 21: a much-needed scission from the frenetic rhythm I had been sprinting to keep up with and the realisation that death and disease aren't exclusively reserved for the elderly. My illness was gradual, creeping, manifesting in pains and symptoms that I would casually brush aside. A pulsating ache in my leg? I'd pulled a muscle. Tiredness? I was run down and working hard on exam prep. Shortness of breath? Well, I needed to work on my fitness levels. It wasn't until I collapsed on the cold tiled steps of my neighbour's house and heard my mother scream that I thought something might be seriously wrong. In that moment, I felt my arms and legs wilting, my body shutting down and my lungs desperately gasping for the air I needed to walk the few steps home. My mother manhandled me back and lay me on the couch, tears streaming down my face as I realised that this might be it: I would die young and miss out on a lifetime of excitement, mistakes and most importantly, love.

The ambulance ride felt eternal, only slightly aided by the aggressive stream of oxygen being pumped up my nose and keeping my body from completely packing in. I had never felt so weak in my entire life. As I was wheeled into A&E, I closed my eyes tight and wished hard that I would survive this, that my parents wouldn't need to bury another child, and that life would be able to happily resume its course for all of us.

"You are suffering from a bilateral pulmonary embolism, Emily. This means that you have blood clots in both of your lungs," said the doctor, countless hours after my admittance. "Your case is quite severe, so we will need to keep you in the High Dependency Unit." He went on to explain that they could surgically 'blast' the clots or I could take blood thinners and hope the clots would dissolve. The former wasn't particularly tested in young people as the illness was so rare in my age group; I opted for the latter. As I was getting ready to be transferred to St Mary's HDU, I heard the doctor discreetly tell my mother that had I not been hospitalised, I would have certainly died in a matter of days.

My recovery was hard. Between the tiredness and physical weakness that made even basic needs impossible without assistance, it was the crippling existential fear that trickled into every layer of my life that was the hardest to overcome. In truth, I still have difficult days, eight years later. But I made sure to think positively, focusing on the second chance I had been given, moving forward with life and embracing the daily lessons I was learning. If this wasn't material for a first tattoo, I wouldn't know what is.

* * *

"You're sure of the placement? The ribs can be a pretty spicy spot, especially for a first tattoo," he asked, positioning the stencil on my cold skin.

"It adds to the meaning," I replied, motioning to my right side. "That's exactly where I had the pain from the clots starving my lung tissue of oxygen." He nodded.

I lay down on my side at his direction, my naked torso sticking to the clingfilm wrapped bed and my breasts falling awkwardly to the side. He told me to breathe normally and stay still. A shiver ran down my spine when I first heard the buzz of the machine, and as I felt the unfamiliar sharp burn of the needle, a sense of peace washed over me. Wincing through the pain, I reflected on my health and everything that had happened since I was hospitalised: the fear, the suffering, the anxiety, but also the growth, the strength and the unconditional love. Every time the needle hit my ribs and reverberated in my skeleton, I embraced the pain as a symbol of life, with the design that was currently being indelibly etched on me as a visual and metaphorical depiction of healing. I knew I needed this, but I had never realised how much until I later saw the boldly outlined floral lung design in the mirror, surrounded by a halo of red skin.

* * *

I didn't wait long before adding to my collection. Mere months later came two photorealistic portraits on the top of my thighs: one of my grandmother in the 1940s and one of my beloved mother in the 1980s. As well as honouring and immortalising two influential, strong and beautiful women in my life, I realised only much later that having them become a part of me was another stepping stone to healing and a sense of identity that I had been craving my whole life, made only more challenging by my near-death experience and the isolation that this period had propelled me into. Decorating my body gave me back a sense of control, the ability to tell my story through beauty and adorn myself with mementos and markers of what I had overcome.

* * *

As an empathic person, life had always been challenging for me, each day bringing with it unpredictable and uncontrollable joy and pain in equal measure, my soul absorbing external stimuli like a sponge that I was unable to ring out or conceal from others. When the first Covid-19 lockdown was mandated, I took it as an opportunity to work on myself, address the darkness that I hoarded inside of me and opened myself up to the light. My body might have healed in the past, but my mind and soul were still suffering. Just like the first time I felt the tattoo needle dance on my skin, I embraced the pain of self-discovery, overdue realisations and mourned for the years I had spent afraid of who I was and fearful of what I would become.

As I had done several times before, I turned to tattoos and art to commemorate this turning point in my life, one that I never thought I would reach. Now, every time I look at the black snake curving up from my left hipbone to my armpit, the delicate female hand holding the Star tarot card symbolising hope, connection to the universe and healing from chaos, I smile. I feel at peace. I have faith in the future.

* * *

I hold the crescent moon pendant against my sternum in front of the bathroom mirror and push the metallic trinket into my skin as hard as I can. It leaves behind a red grooved outline, the flesh in between blanched from the pressure. I cock my head and assess my creation. Perfect. I match up the pendant to the fading outline and press again, hard. This time, the outline lasts longer and I trace its curvatures with my index finger. It will be another 'secret' tattoo, that no one will see unless I am close to or fully naked. One that (most of the time anyway) will be just for me. One that concludes my fertility struggles and

IVF journey, preparing me for the next chapter of my life as a happily single woman and soon, hopefully as a mother. One that I need to have engraved on my skin.

I often think back to my 14-year-old self and know how proud she would be of me, how much I've achieved and how I've conquered things that I would have thought of as insurmountable. When I look at my naked body in the mirror, or I catch a glimpse of my tattoos peeking through my clothes, I take comfort in seeing my story on my skin in a language that can be deciphered only by me and yet admired by others. These scars filled with black ink will never vanish, and I know that they will continue to inspire me to live fearlessly, fully and ferociously till the day I die.

Up next:
Experimental
poetry.

Michał Kamil Piotrowski
Tattoo poem

ₜat**tOO**, a journey into body, into this

transcendental leech, blood into wormholes, into these dimensions now folded. diarrhoea, a verbal flow, elusive, I don't-don't-don't get it. what is an example of transcendental? what are the five values? your second skin, how painful, a shop in the middle of nowhere, is it a cure you've been looking for? time and again, space and time, skin and time, unhinged. I pick my brain cells, I haven't got a single one. am I at one with the world?

tattₒo, a camouflage, a yippy-yay jump into

existence. what's wrong with you today? looking at the black&white flowers, pretty much. a heading, a text, an understanding into body, into transparent veins, into the horns of tomorrow. to put a dot next to a dot next to a dot next to a dot. ascendent. do you believe in astrology? stars and covers, colourful. tattoo, Renaissance, writing a shape of a text into a meaning, onto a belly, how lovely and unintended. skin on skin on skin.

A
dot
next to
a
dot
next to
a
dot.
Meet
tattooist
Erin Hosfield.

Erin Hosfield
What's the weirdest thing you ever tattooed?

It's a common inquiry I receive as a tattooist, but one I'm never sure how to respond to. Is my answer going to be what they're expecting, or will it be a disappointment? The question is often followed by silence, as I have to sort through nearly two decades worth of experiences to find something that might make the cut.

I don't think I can count the few tattoos I did during my apprenticeship, as they're nothing out of the ordinary for beginners. What I practiced on before I tattooed another human might, since in this day and age most apprentices try their hand on synthetic skin rather than cold rubbery slabs of pork flesh. I had rolls of it, and the butcher even tossed in a pig's head when he gave it to me. It was definitely the oddest thing I ever carted around in the trunk of my car, but I never inscribed it with anything. Instead it sat in the refrigerator of my apartment, scaring the life out of my ex-partner each time he opened the door until he made me throw it away.

I've certainly been *asked* to do things one might consider weird, and have come to the conclusion that I've been on the receiving end of those requests mostly because I'm a woman. It's interesting to me that once you're discovered as a tattooist you become a sort of novelty—a party favor—and I was just that many times over. I've been cornered at more than one holiday gathering by a friend of a friend, or a friend of an acquaintance—always someone I didn't know firsthand—and asked if I've ever tattooed a penis, and if I'd consider putting a tattoo on theirs. It was never a party where this type of conversation would be expected, instead it was always some ex-partner's function, the people in attendance all strait-laced corporate types. I'd shrug and tell them no, I haven't, but I probably could. They'd continue with their questions until they were steered away by whomever brought them to the event, and I'd be given the side eye as if I was the one who'd been the initiator.

Those sorts of inquiries didn't only occur outside my workplace, and my studio went through a period of time where we'd receive phone calls asking for the female artist in particular. Usually it was more of the same, with the occasional conversation occurring in person. They'd laugh to their friends and wait for my reaction when they asked if I'd tattoo elephant ears on either side of their dick, and though I'd roll my eyes and tell them sure—for a price—they would never go through with it. Genital requests weren't limited to phalluses, and I recall one particular situation where the client *did* end up with a tattoo. I silently begged her to reconsider her choice before I inscribed her boyfriend's initials on her labia, but she didn't, and he stood close by to watch it unfold.

56

Sometimes I wonder if they're still together, or if she managed to find a new partner with those same initials.

I've definitely turned down a weird request or two, including one I received at the studio in between my apprenticeship and here. A backpiece featuring Jesus giving a blowjob. Now, I didn't feel it blasphemous since I'm not religious, nor did or do I consider oral gratification to be something taboo—I simply didn't want to do it. The man who asked for it became borderline irate when I declined, insisting I had to do whatever he demanded since he was the client and it was my job. I was half afraid I'd be forced to, since my boss at the time only saw dollar signs, but when it became clear he wouldn't pay what was asked I was allowed to proceed with my boundary.

I still don't have a proper answer to this question. Have I been spoiled by the studio I've been at for fifteen plus years, having been granted clientele who mostly want what I like to tattoo most? Do I tell the story about the man who wanted the skeleton of a scorpion, and didn't understand what I meant when I told him scorpions have an exoskeleton, not bones? He insisted they do, and became annoyed when I showed him evidence to the contrary. Do I tell them about other more amusing requests I've simply overheard or saw play out? The man who wanted a shroom, smokin' a blunt, with a cartoon face? Or the person who asked for a stick figure jerking off? Do I detail the years where a common ask was for the tattoo to look wet, with drips trailing from names or pieces of fruit? Or making butterflies look sexy? Perhaps I could list one of my favorite random requests instead. The Crichton Leprechaun—a crudely drawn image labeled an amateur sketch by the news station covering the story. I *did* get to execute that one—on an asscheek. I highly suggest a Google search here—the accompanying video is entertaining.

The more I think about what's considered weird and what isn't, the more hard-pressed I become to find something to report. Are we talking pop culture? Would I like to tattoo an image of Guy Fieri as the grim reaper of Flavortown? Sure, but I haven't been asked to. Are we talking outlandish? Apart from a handful of a few tongue-in-cheek inquiries, I've never actually gotten the chance to make anyone's penis look like a dragon, or put a smiley face on its head. If someone actually wanted a tattoo of a triumphant member or dripping vagina I'd indulge them, but I don't advertise it, so I don't generally receive such requests. What about the bizarre? I only have a few under my belt, including another favorite—a rather large rendering of the Eraserhead baby—but nothing more to add.

'Weird' is subjective. As far as placement goes, body parts aren't weird to me. We all have bodies in different shapes and sizes, but they're mostly the same, and I've seen thousands of them. When it comes to subject matter, I've pretty much seen everything thanks to my time in this industry and the glorious awful thing that is the internet. Nothing fazes me anymore, so ultimately I have to answer that initial question with another question:

"What do you consider 'weird'?"

And now
for
some
skin
deep
fiction.

Sabrina Wolfe

Skin Deep

He got the tattoo when he was 20. The word "penis" up the side of his cock. He said it hurt like fuck and he was already regretting it five minutes in, but he couldn't stop because then he would just have a cock that said "p". It was "pens" when he was flaccid, and "penis" with a hard-on. He thought it was funny. Hell, I thought it was funny too.

We couldn't have sex for three weeks, while it healed. I didn't tell him, but I did a lot of wanking in those weeks. Three weeks without fucking was a ridiculously long time back then. I didn't want him to feel bad about it, so I'd slip off during the day. Started taking lunch time baths. Decided I needed to organise a few books in the bedroom. Spent a long time folding the washing. I had barely shut the door behind me before I was unzipping my jeans.

At that time, we were both hanging out in the flat most of the day. He had a bar job in the evenings and I was working on my dissertation. My course had finished in May and I had all of summer to get my thesis ready. The deadline was September.

We'd sit together at the kitchen table. I'd be reading a book, underlining passages, filling it with different coloured post it notes, jotting a few thoughts down on a spiral bound notepad. He'd be writing song lyrics in a brown moleskin that his mum had given him the Christmas before. There was a dedication in the front: "To our darling son, Somewhere to record all those amazing ideas you have!" and the pages were filled with lyrics about being pissed or high, and lists of words that rhymed with dick, suck and ass.

It was hot in the flat in the summer, up on the top floor of a badly converted Victorian house. The heat rose from everyone else's ovens, toasters and washing machines and settled in our flat, where the windows stuck so badly we rarely bothered to open them, and condensation from drying washing coated the panes. He said his cock was itching too much in boxers while it healed, so he sat there naked, a tube of haemorrhoid cream on the table next to the notebook, and he'd squeeze a bit into his fingers, rub his hands together and then smooth it across the tattoo, sighing in relief as the itch shrank for a few minutes. (I often had to go and check on the washing after that.)

He had a slightly concave chest that I found ridiculously attractive, with very white skin and a few dark hairs muddling around the dip of his breastbone. There was something about it that screamed "tortured bassist in an indie band" and I liked to be on top when we fucked, so I could see him below me, his pale skin accentuated by the dirty navy bedsheets. I'd lean forward and lick the dark hair and imagine him on stage with Radiohead, or perhaps dying of consumption in a Byronic fashion, writing me a last fevered poem before the end finally came.

By September, when I handed in my thesis, his cock had fully healed and the white concave chest had lost some of its appeal. The landlord had come round on a routine inspection and issued us our notice because he'd found the windows stuck shut with condensation, the window frames rotting. It turned out there was a thermostat for underfloor heating that we'd never turned down…

I got a job in London. One of his friends opened a bar in Manchester and needed someone to help promote nights, so he went up there, planning to book his own band in as soon as he could.

There were a few months of occasional expensive train journeys, but neither of us minded too much when they dwindled to nothing. Though the odd text said, "I'll definitely see you next time I'm down, babe," I wasn't too surprised when I saw his band name written up in chalk outside The Kings Head on Upper Street, but he hadn't got in touch.

Years passed and I moved into flats with functioning windows and no condensation, and then into houses, where I was the one in charge of fixing the windows, and then into a house with a husband who did it for me. I moved out of that house when we broke up, and back into a flat, but this time it was all windows, the walls made of glass, and a view out over the Thames right across the city. I left the curtains open when I went to bed at night and watched the light flashing on top of Canary Wharf; I woke to contrails across the sky and planes taking off from City airport.

I wasn't fucking anyone and I only had the odd desultory wank, never furtive, always lying on my bed, in front of the glass walls and looking at the city.

I wasn't fucking anyone and I wasn't missing it, when I walked into a bar one night after work and saw him.

Penis cock.

He was with a couple of old men, and I wondered what he was doing in their company before I fully clocked that he was an old man too. His hair was still dark, with just a few strands of silver shining across the top, and still cut long to his shoulders, but his widow's peak was more obvious, the triangles of skin on either side had extended, scattered with freckles and looking as if they had been too long in the sun. His eyes were puffy, less of the eyeball visible between the drooping lids above and the crinkled bags below. He had a pot belly that was taut and straining against the buttons of his shirt. His shirt had two buttons undone and a sprouting of hair peered out. Brown and curling, with one straight, wiry, white hair on the left-hand side.

I stared at him, not bothering to hide behind my drink, and wondering whether or not to go and say hello, when he looked up, saw me, and walked straight over.

"Fuuuuuck! It really is you, isn't it? You look good, girl, you look good!"

I confirmed it was indeed me, and we went over to his friends. He introduced me with enthusiasm. They'd met "back in the day" he told me (though not as far back as my day, I knew) when they were all "trying to make it in the industry". One was a roadie, now, one worked as a sound technician, and he had a job in an ad agency writing jingles.

We chatted for a bit. I found them boring, but tried to hide it. One of them kept looking down at my cleavage and didn't think I had noticed. I went to the bathroom, re-did my lipstick in the grimy mirror, not because I was interested, but because of pride. Because of not wanting my age to be showing on me as much as his was on him.

When I got back, he'd obviously had a chat to his friends, because they both excused themselves quickly. Had somewhere they had to get to.

He asked me if I wanted another drink and I almost said no. I opened my mouth to say no. I wanted to head back home, to my flat made of glass and my view of Canary Wharf and the contrails. I really almost said no, but somehow there was another drink in my hand, and we were finding a table, and I told myself that I was going to go right after that one.

Except for one thing.

I wanted to know if it was still there.

He'd probably had it lasered off. I mean, you couldn't really go through life with a cock that said "penis". He had an ex, he'd told me, teenage kids that he didn't see as often as he'd like. You can't have a wife and kids and a cock that says "penis". That much was clear to me. But.

I wanted to ask, but it didn't seem like something you could bring up. I bought the next round, told myself that a quick whisky would give me the courage to ask the question – reminded myself of him naked at the kitchen table, rubbing haemorrhoid cream onto his flaking tattoo. We were that close once. Surely there was enough left over from that for me to ask the question without blushing.

We finished that drink and he bought another round. Chatted careers, kids, exes, holidays, TV shows, music. It was his gaze, now, slipping in drink to my cleavage, and mine, I knew, was slipping to his crotch.

"I live quite near here, actually," he said, "I mean, if you wanted, you could – "

I meant to say no. I meant to say no and walk back to the tube, get back to my flat. I meant to say no to the profusion of chest hairs that I didn't recognise. I meant to say no.

But I found myself sitting in a cab with him, heading back to his house, as he leaned against his seatbelt and kissed me with beer in his breath. And I trailed my hand over his stomach, across the waistband of his jeans, and started to undo his fly.

He kissed my neck, and I was holding my breath, my hand reaching inside his boxers. Just as I put my fingers around his cock, the taxi stopped outside his house. He reached across me and opened the door. We lurched out together. I could see the blue and red fabric of his boxer shorts, his jeans gaping open at the fly.

At the front door, he pushed me against the cold UPVC frame and I could feel his cock pressing up against me, but I didn't want to stand outside kissing in the cold. I wanted to see it. I wanted to find out.

He reached around me and unlocked the house. I stumbled as the door opened, lost my footing and grabbed onto the wall to keep myself upright.

I pushed the door shut behind us with my foot. He was trying to take off his coat with one arm, the other tugging at the belt of my jacket. I was too impatient to wait for the coat removal, I grabbed his jeans instead and pulled them down.

I took a step away from him and looked. He stood in the hallway, his coat, cardigan and shirt still on, his black boots surrounded by a puddle of denim, where his jeans lay at his ankles. His legs were long and white, skinny already and made to look even skinnier by the overhang of his stomach. I could see the outline of his hard-on through the red and blue boxers and the uncertainty of what I would or wouldn't find was making me feel turned on in a way I hadn't for years.

I was wet.

I stepped towards him.

I reached out with both hands for the waistband of his boxers and slipped them down.

To set this next one up for you,
here's an email I sent to
Liam Hogan:

What genre would you say Chiaroscuro is? I'm thinking
scifi, but also that seems kind of generic.

best,
Julianne

Liam Hogan
Sat, Aug 26, 5:19 PM (9 days ago)
to me

I'd tend towards "slipstream", I guess!

(note to reader: I don't really know
what to make of this 'slipstream' genre, but you can
Google it if you'd like to find out more)

71

Liam Hogan
Chiaroscuro

I glimpse her through the bead curtain, in the unlit space beyond. It's like watching a silhouette rather than a person: a tall, slender figure, her dark dress tightly fitted.

"I'll be with you in a moment," she says in an exotic singsong.

There's a rattle and she's stood there, half in, half out, lines of beads contouring her body, dimly lit by the red glow of the Chinese lanterns. She is... naked. Naked, but completely covered in abstract patterns. Tattoos.

Not tattoos like any I've seen before; these tattoos are a wall that has been graffitied over and over, swirls and spirals and half-glimpsed shapes, the ink darker with each layer. No inch of flesh remains unmarked, not on the palms of her hands, not even on her forehead between curtains of purple streaked hair.

The sudden downpour that drove me into the festival sideshow eases, the thundering noise softens to a steady patter as she comes towards me. I feel my eyes straying to her breasts and below, wanting to know if she is truly unclothed, not wanting to offend, fighting an urge to escape into the anonymous chaos of the crowds outside.

"Please, be seated," she says, indicating the silk-draped table with its two chairs. I obey and she does the same, arching her back, a languid stretch that has me averting my gaze.

"You can look, you know," she smiles.

I stare into her face. The whites of her eyes are no longer white: deep veins of plum fragment liquid pools of black. It is the most alien thing I have ever seen. She reaches out and strokes my hand.

"So white!" she says.

I feel myself blushing. I blush and burn easily and I've spent the summer hiding from the sun.

"How...?" I mutter.

"How did I end up like this?"

I nod as she runs her dark fingers over the milky paleness of my wrist, the contrast making my skin glow as hers seems to darken, liquid ink devouring the light. *Chiaroscuro*, I think: the interplay of light and dark.

"Some say I incurred a tattooist's curse. Others say I was born this way. Some refuse to believe it's real and try to rub off what they take for body paint. These men I do not like. But you? You have no tattoos?"

I shake my head.

"Ah." She cocks her head to the side. "We are unbalanced, you and I. I am dark; too dark, perhaps, and you — you are a blank page. You show nothing of yourself, protected in your ivory tower, your skin unmarked by the passage of time, of life."

I tense my arm to bring it back to me, away from this naked apparition. In a world where nearly everyone you meet has a tattoo, this... this is still too much.

"Wouldn't you like one?" she murmurs, her fingers tightening their grip.

"Like one... what?" I ask, my glance falling once again to her slight breasts, embarrassment mixing with a stomach-plunging thrill as I see her nipples are now more prominent, are now erect.

"A tattoo!" she laughs and I look away as the laughter jiggles what I had been staring at.

"No," I say, tucking my wrist into my body. "I can't stand... needles."

She shakes her head, soft and slow. "No needles."

And then she's kneeling on the mat by my side, looking up with those bizarre eyes, her hand outstretched, palm up.

I let her pull my hand back towards her. She closes her eyes and hums. I feel it rather than hear it and it takes a moment before I understand; she's imitating the buzz of a tattoo gun. At least, that's what I imagine it might sound like. I shift uncomfortably in my seat. As the moment drags on my thoughts turn carnal, the sound is having an effect at the very core of me.

"There," she says, letting go of my hand as the hum ends. "Balance."

She reaches out and twists my arm. On the underneath is a black smudge that even as I watch begins to unfurl, to swirl into a pair of roses, curled around each other, one light, one dark, the whole an intricate circle of thorns and leaves and petals. She holds out her forearm, twists it to match mine, and I'm seeing double, an echo in

75

reverse: the same design but etched in an *absence* of ink, a negative.

In the spaces between I see pale flesh, pasty white. A part of her is now mine and a part of me is hers.

"Look," she says proudly. "I am Yin and you, Yang."

I rub at the mark, disbelieving, but it does not come off, it will not come off. She presses her arm tight against mine, presses herself tight against me, and I realise I am a very, very, long way from home.

Up next:
A short story in the horror genre by
a writer whose bio says:

Callum Henderson is a carbon-based life who has been
writing avidly since nineteen-canteen. He is Scottish,
and aware that the condition is incurable.

Callum Henderson
Semantics

Nick rubbed the fresh ink etched on his skin and frowned at the word he saw there:

AGONY

"It's the strangest thing," he muttered. "Where did it come from?"

Nick had been out on the piss with his mates the night before, and had woken up that morning with the new tattoo scrawled in thick black lettering on the back of his arm.

The thing was, he didn't remember getting it. He didn't even remember *deciding* to get it.

His girlfriend, Siobhan, rolled her eyes at him.

"Couldn't you have gotten something nicer?" she asked. "It's a bit kinky, isn't it?"

Nick had always wanted a tattoo.

His pal Kyle had one. He'd been in the navy, and he'd been showing it off all night — flexing his enviably-ample bicep.

"Did it hurt?" Nick had asked him.

Kyle had taken a mocking swig of lager and replied: "You don't know the meaning of the word."

Nick was afraid of needles. So he'd never had the courage to step into a studio and take the plunge.

He must have gotten this done when he'd been drunk. Yeah. He must've wandered into one of those open-all-hours tattooists and passed out while they were inking him.

Of course. That made sense. Must have done.

AGONY

He shook his head. The word had no meaning. It didn't speak to him on any emotional or spiritual level, didn't remind him of anything he wanted commemorated. Of all the tattoos he could have chosen, he wouldn't have chosen this one.

It felt like he'd been vandalised.

"Goodnight, you daft bugger," said Siobhan, pecking his cheek and turning off the bedside light.

Nick sighed, rolled over in his bed, and drifted off to sleep.

Ah well. Like it or not, he'd have to live with it now.

* * *

The next day, the tattoo had moved.

When Nick woke up his arm was unblemished. At first, he thought the whole thing had been a weird dream. But then he looked down while flossing and saw that, somehow, incredibly, it had migrated in the night to sit on the inside of his left thigh.

It didn't make any sense. Tattoos were supposed to be permanent. They were supposed to stay put. That was the whole point.

Mildly concerned, he tried scrubbing it off in the shower; first with a sponge, then with a loofa, and finally with his fingernails.

Despite all his efforts, the word remained indelible:

AGONY

Was it the name of a band? Nick couldn't think of any. Besides, he'd never cared for heavy metal.

Troubled, Nick went into work. He had a deadline coming up: new logo for a publisher that specialised in medical journals.

Yet try as he might, he just couldn't seem to concentrate on the spread of fonts he'd designed last week. Three nasty syllables seemed to be glued to his palette.

And his leg itched. Badly.

Nick went to bed early that night, praying that the tattoo wouldn't be there when he woke up again.

His prayers were answered. In a manner of speaking.

* * *

The alarm sounded. Nick threw off his duvet and ran to the mirror.

His eyes bulged like poached eggs when he saw his own reflection.

Now the tattoo was on his *forehead*:

AGONY

Nick knew he should tell Siobhan what was happening. But somehow, whether through pride, embarrassment, or sheer disbelief, he just couldn't manage it. The word lodged in his throat, and stayed put.

Instead, he wrapped a bandage around his head and went straight into the office; alarming his co-workers all morning with his manic jollity.

"Cut myself shaving!" he blurted out, whenever anyone asked, or even *looked* like they *wanted* to ask, about his dressings.

There was enough white showing in his eyes to discourage his colleagues from further inquiry.

When it came to lunchtime, Nick was planning on sneaking into the toilet to take off his bandages and inspect his head.

But before the clock struck one, he was floored by a sharp pain; like a hot ice pick piercing his skull.

He grit his teeth and buried his face into the crook of his arm, but the throbbing ache only intensified until he let out a howl. He couldn't help it. Everyone turned to look at him.

"Migraine?" his boss asked sympathetically. She'd been watching Nick writhing from the water cooler for half a minute.

Nick nodded, hoping she was right, and asked if he could go home.

The whole office exhaled the moment he left.

* * *

On the bus back, the pain stopped as quickly as it had come. Relieved, Nick kneaded his clammy brow, and then gasped when he saw:

AGONY

The word had jumped onto the palm of his hand.

He was so shocked he almost missed his stop. He hared out of the bus as the doors were closing and ran straight to his semi-detached.

Rattling his keys, he elbowed his way in, ran up to his room, and began frantically Googling 'Tattoo Removal.' The search results were unanimously scary and expensive. But Nick didn't care.

Three days ago he'd been scared of getting a tattoo.

Now he was afraid of *having* one.

By six he was poised to book an appointment, prepped to have it flayed off his flesh with a potato peeler, if necessary. He went to get his credit card from his coat pocket —

And his hand started to seize up. A bitter, biting cold crept from his wrists all the way to the ends of his fingertips. It scourged, and gnawed, and numbed the limb all the way to the bone.

Excruciating. Searing. *Agony.*

Nick yelled, and over the sound of his own shrill cries he heard keys rattle in the lock of his front door. Then footfalls up the staircase. Then Siobhan, chalk-white, mouth wide, burst into the room.

"What is it!?" she shrieked, racing to his side. "What's wrong!?"

"MY HAND!" Nick raved, waving it before her face. "THE TATTOO! IT—*Glomph!*"

He felt the icy chill depart his hand in a prickle of pins and needles. But as it did so, he began salivating like a dog. His gums swelled while his tongue inflated with anaphylactic speed.

"*MUMF!*" Nick slurred helplessly.

Siobhan shook her head at him, her own mouth pencil sketch thin by contrast. Stumbling to his feet, Nick ran to the bathroom mirror and almost fainted on the spot when he saw:

AGONY

The words were graffiti, stamped on his swollen tongue.

Mocking him.

Siobhan was shouting something, but Nick couldn't hear her. He had to act quickly. Only one way to be sure. One way to be safe.

He fumbled the en suite drawer open and his questing hands closed over cool stainless steel.

Shaking, Nick pried the blades of the scissors open and lay his tongue between them.

He'd only have to snip off the end to sever the damn thing. But he'd have to be fast. He hoped it was sharp enough. He didn't want to botch it. To have to keep cutting.

Sweat beaded his top lip as Siobhan tried to stop him. But before he could snap the edges of the shears together, something impossible happened:

AGONY

The two of them watched, transfixed, as the tattoo moved before their very eyes, sliding along the top of the worming pink muscle and dropping down his throat.

Like a black spider, trying to find a new home.

Nick gulped. He swallowed, and swallowed, and swallowed until the tears ran. But there was nothing he could do. He couldn't keep that word down. It was rising like bile: up, up, up—

Until there was only one place left for it to go.

Nick dropped to his knees, and screamed, and he didn't stop screaming until the ambulance arrived…

* * *

It was the strangest thing.

And it became one of those unexplained phenomena — diligently documented in medical journals. For years after, experts marvelled at the MRI of the patient's brain.

The doctors were used to seeing spots, lumps, and shadows.

But not *writing*.

AGONY

Nick knew the meaning of the word, all right.

On our blog, Meredith MacLeod Davidson wrote:

"My short story 'Illuminated' seeks to explore the sometimes-conflicting elements of art, death, creativity, gender, ritual, capitalism, communion with other persons, the internet and social media, permanence, and ownership. It represents a segment of my ongoing interrogation of internalized ideas surrounding art, spirituality, and politics, and I hope it duly honors tattoo as an art form and tattoo artists as incredible practitioners of a (divine) creative medium."

Meredith MacLeod Davidson
Illuminated

"Think you've got a no-show today?" Stotz yelled over his shoulder and the buzz of his tattoo gun.

Amara ran a hand through her hair, frustrated. "Hope not. If this chick bails, I'm eating air tonight."

Ever since Amara had approached tattooing full-time, her livelihood was wholly dependent on her clients' whims. Stotz didn't pay her, but he also didn't charge for studio space, and at least here, unlike the predatory shop where she had apprenticed, she had complete artistic autonomy.

Today's client had messaged Amara with a custom idea over Instagram:

> *Amara,*
>
> *Your style would be perfect for my tattoo, an illustration from an illuminated manuscript. I am not looking for strict replication – I want to give you as much creative freedom as possible. Please let me know when we can schedule an appointment.*
>
> *Giselle*

The image had followed. An exquisite swirling, arcing, blue letter detailed with flowers, a sexless monk playing a violin with a small dog at its feet, and vines hoisting bright red blooms toward the heavens, where clouds and sunrays disguised an exultant cherub.

Amara woke her phone for the time, anxiously awaiting Giselle. She checked her inks again. She had selected a palette of blues, careful to ensure the tattoo would look rich and deserving of its pigments, not melt with time into an effigy of bruised skin.

The bell which measured the comings and goings of the shop heralded the entrance of a middle-aged woman with silver-blonde hair in a ponytail, harsh with a ferocity of steps. She extended her arm, "Giselle. Sorry I'm late." She shrugged by way of explanation.

Amara seated Giselle at her station, then sat across from the woman and started her spiel:

"Let's talk placement." Amara pulled out pre-printed stickers of her drawing, executed in various sizes ranging from five to ten inches tall. "And size?" She extended the handful of sticker-prints to Giselle.

Giselle considered. Amara watched.

Amara had found that half of tattooing was simply creating space for your client. Some people couldn't care less what was etched on their body, but others, *like Giselle,* took the process quite seriously. They made a ritual of it.

Once decided, the silver-headed woman watched Amara studiously as she worked, cleaning the skin, laying the sticker and peeling it back to reveal a purple shadow-trace of the tattoo.

Amara eyed Giselle. "Ready?" Giselle nodded enthusiastically. With a plunge of the needle Amara began, remaining steady through Giselle's initial flinch, her focus wholly now on the work.

For the first hour, she registered only the twin buzzings of needles in the shop, a weak chatter between Stotz and his client. Giselle was stone: the ideal canvas, breathing softly, but still. Amara slipped into a trance as first she outlined, in navy, plotting mentally the details to follow in progressively lighter shades of blue.

It wasn't until around the third hour, as Amara was wetting her needle in vibrant ultramarine, that Giselle spoke.

"I was reading," she began. Amara nodded. When a client was ready to talk, you took it in pace.

"Well – do you know what an illuminated text is?"

Amara bit her lip, "I mean, I learned what they were after your message. They're like the old religious books this drawing's from?"

Giselle nodded, a thin smile at her lips, "Precisely. There were monks in the Middle Ages who would spend their entire lives doing nothing but hand-illustrating these books."

Amara pressed the needle's head to skin, shading.

"Printmaking was significantly less accessible than it is today, of course. Every book was made entirely by hand, the inks distilled from precious minerals. Gold, silver."

Amara tipped her chin to demonstrate her attention.

Giselle's gaze flicked between artist and arm. "So, they're doing this study on corpses, somewhere in Europe. And one of the remains was from a middle-aged woman, from about the 12th century."

Amara nodded, half-listening, intent on getting just the right gradient of blue down the letter.

"There's this misconception amongst historians," Giselle said and shifted her position while Amara wiped away ink, "that women weren't involved in printmaking back then, that it was men only."

"Why's that?" Amara buzzed an old needle in distilled water and unwrapped a new one.

"Because these artists never signed their work!"

Amara looked up just then.

"It was a humility thing, work in service to God, what-have-you." Giselle waved her hand. "Because there were no signatures, the assumption, somehow, was that women weren't involved at all."

Amara frowned, thinking, inexplicably, of her Instagram account.

"They looked at the plaque of her teeth. This nun from the Middle Ages. And when they dissolved it, this calcified gunk that collected in her mouth over her lifetime, they found fragments of lapis lazuli."

"The stone?" Amara asked, taking her needle now to the feathers of the cherub's wings.

Giselle affirmed. "At the monasteries, they would take lapis lazuli and grind it down to powder, yielding this rare, highly pigmented blue. An ink worth more than gold."

"No shit," Amara murmured, developing an etch of blue lines: the ephemeral angel wings melting into cloud.

"Yes! Only the most holy of texts were developed with these inks: blue, silver, gold. The implication of them finding lapis lazuli fragments in this woman's dental tartar, is that *she* was in fact an artist. A woman!"

"That's beautiful," Amara granted.

Giselle glanced down at her arm, blood pebbling at the surface where the needle had passed. "Oh, it is beautiful."

Amara grinned, quite pleased with how the piece was going. "Almost done," she said, adding highlights in white.

Gently wiping the blood and leaking ink away with a wet towel, Amara revealed the finished marking – perhaps her best tattoo yet. She held her breath; Giselle gasped. Blue luminous, held forever in skin.

Stotz came over to look. "Alright, girl!" He shook his head appreciatively. "Make sure you get a pic of that for the shop site." He clapped Amara's shoulder with an ink-muddied hand; the black smeared on her shirt.

Giselle fondled her purse, producing a wad of cash - $20s folded, loose in the bag. She counted them twice, then extended them to Amara. "It is *exactly* what I wanted." A streak of silver hair escaped the tie, embellishing her face.

Amara walked Giselle through the aftercare. "Would you mind if I took some pictures?"

"Not at all!" Giselle said and Amara led her over to a blank wall, where she kept a ring light for just such photography. She did a quick photoshoot with her phone. Giselle held her arm stiff against her body to best display Amara's work. Happy with the captures, Amara turned off the light, bandaged the tattoo, and walked Giselle to the door.

Giselle leaned in suddenly, cradling Amara's neck with one arm. "I will wear your art about the world with *reverence.*"

Amara blushed. Giselle left. The bell echoed.

Amara ambled back to her station, perusing her phone for the best image to share on her tattoo artist page. Surely this would be the tattoo that propelled her to Instagram stardom – she pictured followers multiplying.

So engrossed she was in editing the image and drafting her caption that Amara did not register the cacophony of sound emerging from the street.

"Holy shit!" The buzzing of Stotz's machine cut out.

Amara jerked her head up from her phone. "What?"

Stotz dropped his needle, rushed toward the window. His client remained in the chair, a hand clasped over her mouth.

"Isn't that –" Stotz trailed off, his finger bent almost backward pressed against the windowpane.

In the street: A car parked diagonally across the lanes, hazards flashing. A smear of red leading to a limp body splayed across the pavement. At its neck, catching the eerie neon blue light from the approaching police car, a head of hair so light, it looked silver.

Next up
Harriet Bradshaw:

"The story you're about to read is fiction, in the realm of magical realism. It's a commentary on life from a close and honest observer. It's about young love, toxic romance, growing up and parenthood. Because every tattoo seems to have a story, what if it could tell you exactly what that story was?"

Harriet Bradshaw
The Magpie Tattoos

I was born through cuts to flesh, blood mixed with ink, moving across the skin. A sharp chilling trilling, scratching, and moaning awoke me. My new home. I flexed my wings across her collar bone, as she moved and followed our reflection in wonder. Feathers detailed in fine black lace like rhythms, the penmanship of an artist.

I was monochrome except for a flash of blue in the tail and one detail. Clasped in my beak at her throat was a single red ruby in the shape of a heart.

I took her in before absorbing myself. My owner. Her name was Ruby, and she was my precious gem. The light spread across her flesh, so her bones appeared like structures beneath silk. They caused shadows to dance on her damp and clammy skin. Her hair brushed my claws as she swept away the wisps with long fingers dipped in red polish, eyes wide in the dim room walled in scrawl. She tentatively touched me, delicate and sore. Pride in her smile. As she laughed her whole body shook, so even her ears pierced in flesh and metal danced and chimed.

I was magnificent. And she delighted in me. And she was mine. All of her. My Ruby.

But when he appeared beside us in the mirror, I froze. His name was Oran. Her keeper. And the keeper of another bird. He rolled up his sleeve to reveal my equal, my beloved, my nemesis, her wings stretched like mine but this time they fluttered across the fingers. She was daintier than me, and instead of a red heart an emerald one was pincered against the skin in that black billed beak. Claws like tendrils wrapped around the underside of Oran's wrist. And she was beautiful and frightening. And I was ensnared and jealous.

Oran lifted his hand to Ruby's neck, stroking his fingers delicately across my tender feathers, and that's where we met. A pair of birds fashioned from the same craftsmanship, the same artistry and hand. Twins in finesse, but different in detail.

"Magpies mate for life" was their reason for matching body art. A young couple of "love birds" ready to commit. Oran and Ruby, Ruby and Oran. Green and red were their colours by name and now etched like flags on their skin. Now inseparable, holding each other's hearts in their mouths like precious stones, the possessiveness of young love. But too young, some would say. Barely legal during their final year of school. And it was telling that day when the yelling broke the house. I realised I wasn't universally cherished as Mother screamed at "that disgusting tattoo" emblazoned across her daughters' neck.

"What did that boy make you do?"

As if Ruby was caged.

To some I was a controversial mark to be concealed behind skin toned paste. But Ruby loved me. Showing me off at the cafe where she waitressed on Saturdays. I knocked against her chokers and thick metal chains, heavy on her delicate skin like the eyeliner and mascara of her lashes.

Her friends loved to comment on us. They laughed at Oran, asking if his tattoo symbolised how Ruby wrapped him around her little finger. Oran's weak smile ignited a flicker in his eyes, which should have been a warning.

Such wildness "must be love" the friends concluded as dusk fell on the hormones of summer. There they sat cross-legged in a circle around a forbidden barbecue, its smoke fading into the dusty light as embers burnt.

I called out in sweet song to Oran's magpie. She humoured me with her beady eyes before looking crestfallen. Eyes of sorrow, tinged with anger. I wanted her, I wanted us to be etched together, wrapped around each other in patterns. But I would come to fear my equal, the bird drawn and scratched into flesh for me. Made for me to love.

My desire was almost lived out as we entwined that night beneath the canopy of silver dipped leaves, as the moonlight witnessed the satisfied moans of young lovers pinned against a tree, a hand around a throat in some sort of erotic dance. But the moans turned to panic and tears that echoed across the tiles of a school bathroom, as a plastic stick with a plus sign fell onto the cubicle floor.

"What have you done, Ruby?!"

As if creating a child was the woman's fault.

Ruby's stomach, her face and ankles, swelled with a heaviness drawing unwanted attention and gossip until flesh ripped with primal groans. Screams and a seismic cry marked the moment when everything changed. Ruby's tears of joy and fatigue, wonder and fascination rolled onto me as her baby, wrapped in blood and mucus and mess, rested on her chest getting brighter with every new breath. Oran had left the room.

They called her Maggie. Baby Maggie-magpie. Her tiny fat fingers would grasp at my claws and press my heart like a button. Baby Maggie's eyes, set in pudgy fresh unmarked skin, began absorbing my shapes and lines as she grew and dribbled with curiosity. She was always happiest nestled up against Ruby's warmth and smell, and I felt protective over her, so small and innocent. Those round, fat arms would rest across my wingspan as her heavy eyelids and lashes bobbed lower and lower into a deep sleep. I'd live for the child's giggle but mourn the grizzles and crying that broke every heart and every sleep cycle.

But Ruby and Oran's love was far from the gentle breath of their baby. The fatigue of sleepless nights. The arguments turned to bitterness as a couple of barely adults tried to play house in a flat not fit to cage two birds.

Oran spoke of an imagined "successful" life he claimed he'd lost. He fancied himself as a writer, like Ruby, but rich. An aspiration she was charmed by when they first met. But that now felt like a lifetime ago. His complaints about working two "crappy" jobs to pay the bills had become exhausting.

"Write about it. The best writing comes from experience," Ruby dared to suggest before Oran's fist went through the plasterboard bruising the bristles and feathers of my beautiful counterpart.

Ruby would cry at the name "bitch". Oran would cry too. But the "I'm so sorry", followed by the weeping began to tire, when "sorry" became a habit rather than an exception. The disappointment was like a wheel, a trusted cycle, with no escape as there was a child to shield and dress and wash and take for walks and playtime in the park.

And yet, despite her friends and family's advice and judgement, Ruby stayed with Oran. Waiting for redemption? Or maybe she simply didn't know how to leave the "love of her life", the father of her child, the emotional investment.

She stayed with him when he said her talking exhausted him, that they weren't compatible anymore. She stayed with him when he repeatedly came home late and ignored her. She stayed with him when he didn't conceal his rage. She stayed with him when he compared her body to other women's. When he picked apart the way she looked and the clothes she wore and how she should cut her hair. She even stayed with him when he had to get checked at the clinic. A drunken one-night stand outside the back of the restaurant amongst the smell of scraped rotting leftovers and tarmac was tinged with regret until it wasn't a one-off after all. But Ruby's choice to sacrifice herself over and over again drained her. And this life with Oran had changed her.

By the time Maggie had started school, Ruby was surviving only on the energy she had for her daughter. The little girl in bright red socks and butterflies in her hair. Ruby's frown was more severe, her cheeks had hollowed, she was now frosty in self-preservation. But I remember the day the facade cracked like ice beneath heavy boots.

Ruby had laughed wildly at something Oran had said, weary of his complaints and empty apologies. And in a whisper of a moment, I felt a sudden pressure on my lines and limbs, a suffocating weight, and the beady eyes of another so close to torment pressing in on me. It only lasted seconds, but felt like an age. When Oran stopped squeezing it was as if he'd touched an iron, he'd recoiled so vividly with a fear I'd never seen in his eyes before. It was as if he had awoken for the first time to the destruction he was capable of.

"Ruby, I…" But he never finished, interrupted by the sobs of a seven-year-old observer and Ruby's sharp breath as she clutched her throat and stroked my wings. She knew enough was enough.

"Can me and Maggie come and stay with you?"

An old school friend put them up, mum and daughter seeking refuge in the depths of the night. The clothes in rucksacks eventually migrating to the wardrobes as a temporary fix rolled on and on. Hospitality bringing new life to all parties.

I watched Ruby let go of a relationship she'd already grieved. She was lighter in the way she walked and spoke. She smiled at herself in the mirror. She started to take care of what she wore and ate. She made friends at the school pick up and after work as if suddenly the world was bigger than Oran. She even went on a dating app and enjoyed the attention.

But during her new years of freedom, my life darkened. Ruby had begun to hide me away. Gone was the supposed free spirit of her youth that nailed her image to a particular theme. Now the dark eye liner and pink hair, the lace up boots and piercings, the chokers and heavy chains, only existed in photographs. Her renewed style was floral and pastel, safe with a hint of fun in her choice of earrings. A change in look she felt came with the restraints of being an adult. Working in a school as a teaching assistant had created a permanence to my concealment. It was easier to leave the scarf and make up on when she got home. But the job was an excuse. I began to feel like a literal scar of a life that was. Snippets of news about Oran still got back to Ruby through their now teenage daughter. He'd finished an English degree, then a masters, prodigal son bankrolled by the parents who felt he'd fallen in love below his station with Ruby. Parents who were content now he'd got a steady girlfriend to go with a steady job in banking, laughing off his "childish" dream of being a writer.

But Ruby hadn't given up on her dream to be published. It was all she had of her past that wasn't wrapped up in him. Her ability to write. Every moment of precious quiet, for which there were few as a single parent, Ruby would tap away on her phone. Easier to conceal than a notebook.

"Who you messaging, Mum?" Maggie, not a baby anymore, would ask stretched out on the sofa as she listened to music whilst flicking through her revision notes. To be young again, Ruby had thought looking at the beautiful adolescent she'd grown and nurtured and done her best to keep grounded. Proud she'd grown to be a studious young thing who was punctual and knew clever words.

"Nosy Maggie. I'm actually writing. Kids story. About a little bird who doesn't know how to fly."

Ruby had gently touched her throat and I felt her cool fingers shudder down my spine making me jump for the first time in a long time.

When Maggie started to cry, Ruby dropped her phone and rushed to comfort her daughter, finally coaxing the news out of her by stroking her hair. Ruby didn't know why Oran's wedding irritated her so much. She wasn't invited of course, but didn't blame the bride who was suspicious of Oran's previous flames. But Maggie attended, describing her father's expense, from the venue to the favours, as "obscene", frustrated such financial care hadn't been given to her own needs for university.

It was a September afternoon when the last chain of their union, Ruby and Oran, Oran and Ruby, was broken, scrubbed out. Oran had casually dropped it into conversation as he picked Maggie up to drive her to university. Flexing his fingers. His empty, plain fingers. He explained how it had hurt like hell.

"Don't expect that from lasers. But you know, the Mrs thought it was time. Too personal, people and clients always ask for the story and I have to explain it was a stupid childhood dare. Can't believe you still have yours."

Ruby smashed a mug against a wall in solitude that afternoon. Then we both wept.

Alone now for the first time in years, as the days ticked by she watched trashy television and ate her way through most of the takeaway menus in her kitchen drawer. Her daughter was gone, so was Oran's magpie, and yet she knew Oran himself still had an unhealthy hold over her.

By week three her school friend intervened.

"Pursue a hobby, take a year out, do something, something for you, but don't let him win."

By week four she was writing again, this time drawing too.

But it wasn't until after her daughter had finished her degree and had moved on from her first job that Ruby got a small publishing deal. It was by sheer fluke that a child at the school where Ruby was an assistant had a mum in the business. Ruby had returned to the story about the bird who couldn't fly and tested it on the school children she supported. They loved it.

I was on display once more. The freedoms of an author to be more expressive. And I saw the old Ruby return. Independent, free, light. She owned the room once again. But it was a confidence easily shattered with a simple message from Oran.

"Thinking of our daughter, little Maggie magpie on her birthday and the day she came into the world. Saw your book. Funny you're still hung up on the birds. Well done, I guess. Always saw you as a serious writer rather than a kids' author. But never judge a book by its cover. Keep it real, O x"

Ruby screamed, falling to the floor and scratching at my wings. "Enough!" she cried out as she wept grasping her throat in the mirror. "Enough!"

The man at the appointment kept asking if she was sure. But Ruby was sure. The first scrape was the most painful. Then slowly I just felt numb.

And here we are, at the end, the final lines and shades of a magpie disappearing under the craftsmanship that once made me. His hand more withered than when I was first etched onto Ruby's skin. He mutters his pity that Oran had erased his other masterpiece. But doesn't say much more. As the final fixes scratch and jitter across Ruby's skin, blood wiped away, the eyes of my maker look wet as if holding back a tear.

Ruby walks to the mirror, and scans the details across her collarbone. Not erased but transformed. Black feather outlines are now filled with colour, and not a heart but a smoky red fire is clasped in my beak. Rather than a magpie staring back at me, I see myself as a phoenix rising out of the flames.

Exit
fiction
zone.

Louisa Mastromarino
Tattoo Trials

Tattoo, scoundrel, broke my heart with one hundred layers of stale ink.

He broke my senses so much, he toiled me deep in red wine.

I love it though, the pain, the wound, the sound of the foiled robbery.

I still have some morbid leakage down the center. The heart cracked.

I asked the King of Tattoos to stake a heart on my chest.

My real one cracked a mile ago when Darla left me, broke.

I vowed to rake in the mud no more with this last one cursed.

The tattoo before, I wore down my left knee to honor my dead mother.

I am a soldier, a warrior, a king too of tattoo freedom.

Every time I still the death of a lover, I rise to remember her swollen,

bruised, and abandoned in bodily humiliation.

My mother too, was a warrior down, crushed by my father's footsteps in steep waters.

Risen, he finds himself memorialized on the back of my right leg, dead as a doornail, driven by deranged girls himself in summertime.

So lashed was he with tattoos that he inspired me to stoke
my own.
Now, I rise with love to begin to heal the splintered scar
and the
bleeding sash of time's infinite robberies.
Time heals all wounds I am told whether they are cracked
by feminine
wayfaring ways or cracked by a mother's jewels and
cookies in the sink.

I am no king of comfort as I tend to mend my scarred body
now, bruised by the Tattoo King
in Cupid's game and distilled by lovers entombed in
droves of trampled fields.

Up next: Dominic Lyne
Genre: Transgressive fiction

Dominic Lyne
The Phoenix and a Magpie

What do they represent, these messages
drilled into my skin as permanent markers
of a journey in a body that does not feel my own.
I was born into this skin, pale and expectant,
these lines and colours tell tales of independence;
of hours spent in meditation
as meaning is given permanence
and that bastard flesh of youth is bled away.

My first symbolised life and death.
Originally as symbols, and then a skull with flames,
the beginning and the end, cycles of rebirth.
The phoenix rising from the ashes,
or the autumnal leaves falling around the serpent;
a nod towards Eden, that I knew before knowledge,
I just hadn't learnt the truth of my childhood
and for that more protections needed to amass.

Then when the storms came and the earth cracked,
devouring the Tree of life,
I tattooed a magpie for sorrow on my chest,
a reminder that you cannot just keep restarting.
Because these are not just memories,
they are legacies, stories painted into flesh.
A roadmap of my existence, of attempted ownership
until my death.

115

On our blog, Maria Jastrzębska wrote:

"I was born in Warsaw and came to the UK the child of Polish immigrants. Growing up between two cultures has formed the backdrop to most of what I write. I'm interested in those places or moments where people from different cultures or backgrounds meet and I believe everyone crosses different thresholds one way or another, even within the same country."

Maria Jastrzębska

Iwonka

The first tattoo I ever saw was not
a lotus, beating wings, astrology
with suns and moons, not Muhammad Ali,
clinching Sonny Liston in a headlock.
It wasn't Buffy teenage vampire slayer,
a Celtic knot, or lines by e.e cummings,
a lover's name, a spider, skull or Sphinx,
not a wolf's jaw gaping or even a prayer.
No. A row of numbers inked in green
is what I saw while trying not to look,
imagining the needle's stab, her scream,
blood dots along her arm, the force it took.
None of us dared ask who held her still.
She never spoke of when she lived in hell.

An essay:
Civilized
people
don't
do
that
to
their bodies.

Karla Linn Merrifield
Of Lightning Bolts and a Palm Tree

I've never had any desire to get a tattoo.

After all, I already have a birthmark on my right ring finger. Why add to the body markings? And, if the pain entailed in getting one weren't enough to deter me, there's the cultural baggage I've carried with me most of my life. As a kid in the late 50s and early 60s, tattoos were the province of "greasers" and "hoods"—those lowlife boys from across the tracks and their kin, the muscle car jockeys. My exposure to real-life tattoos was limited to movies in which sailors got drunk and then tattooed in exotic ports or in the pages of *National Geographic* with its pictorials of Māori people with elaborate face tattoos. Of course, back then any such natives were largely viewed as savages, so the message to me was: Civilized people don't do that to their bodies.

Also, at a young age I had already learned from my parents that tattooing is what the Nazis did to the Jews during World War II—marking each of their victims with a tattoo on their wrists as an identification badge, a horrific practice I once saw with my own eyes on the arm of an elderly woman who was ahead of me in line at the Maxie's Delicatessen across the street from my home. She reached out to pay for her halvah and the telltale numbers emerged from behind her left sleeve. I can still see the few blue numerals in my mind's eye. It still shakes me.

I was in my teens then and dating a Jewish boy. He explained that in the Jewish religion, tattoos are a no-no. Although tattoos have become more and more mainstream recently, and some Jews have relaxed their thoughts about them, "tattoos are still overwhelmingly perceived as inconsistent with the teaching of Jewish tradition," according to *My Jewish Learning* (https://www.myjewishlearning.com/article/the-tattoo-taboo-in-judaism/). The tattoo taboo remains, rooted as it is in Jewish law articulated in Leviticus 19:28: "You shall not make gashes in your flesh for the dead, or incise any marks on yourselves: I am the LORD."

Of course, there are exceptions to every rule. Little did I know, until today, there's a family-owned "centuries-old tattoo business" in the heart of Jerusalem! Curious? Check it out: https://www.nytimes.com/2022/04/15/world/middleeast/jerusalem-tattoo-artist.html.

As to other religions' views on tattooing… Christianity in general has no specific prohibition of tattoos, although individual Christians might take issue, and Catholics codified their stance on the practice during the Crusades, ruling that tattooing is permissible. Hindus permit body art but Muslims see it as a sin, and one of their hadiths (sayings of Mohammed) curses those who create them as well as those who have them inked onto their bodies. There are no references in the Qur'an to tattoos. Today, they're still frowned upon, mostly from a health perspective: HIV/AIDS, hepatitis, and other diseases that can be transmitted through tattooing.

Look closer and you'll learn that tattoos are a far more ancient art form than dealt with by the old religions:

The earliest evidence of tattoo art comes in the form of clay figurines that had their faces painted or engraved to represent tattoo marks. The oldest figures of this kind have been recovered from tombs in Japan dating to 5000 BCE or older.

In terms of actual tattoos, the oldest known human to have tattoos preserved upon his mummified skin is a Bronze-Age man from around 3300 BCE. Found in a glacier of the Ötztal Alps, near the border between Austria and Italy, 'Otzi the Iceman' had 57 tattoos. (From "A Brief History of Tattoos" on Welcome Collection, https://wellcomecollection.org/articles/W9m2QxcA AF8AFvE5.)

Even had I known that years ago, I would still have viewed tattooing as barbaric, inappropriate in my narrow white, middle-class American culture.

It wasn't until well into adulthood I actually met someone with a tattoo. A co-worker and eventual bestie had a tiny one on her ankle; she now sports five designs scattered along her limbs and torso. In my late 60s I had two lovers with one tattoo each—a tall ship on one man's left forearm, another with a palm tree on his left bicep. The latter ended up the focus of a poem, "#62: Sparky with the Palm-Tree Tattoo."

I was on the *Queen Mary 2* for a 108-day world voyage to twenty-two ports, along with 2400 other passengers and hundreds of staff from around the world. After the first couple of weeks I realized how many tattoos kept passing within my view—they kept catching my eye in their variety and placement. And, since my camera was always at hand, I began to "collect" them in a series of photographs. It started one evening when a man at the bar next to me wore an island scene on his forearm. I asked permission to photograph it and he proudly held out his arm for the shots. Then, a waiter from the Philippines had one peeking out of his shirt sleeve. When I inquired about it, he put down his serving tray and began to undress, taking off his jacket and shirt to proudly display portraits of all four Beatles, skillfully depicted in blue ink on his light brown skin with nary an eyelash missing and even a shimmer it seemed in John Lennon's spectacles!

I grew to appreciate the art of the tattoo, to admire the artistry and imagination of the tattoo artist, of which there are three in my village of 9,800 folks, an abundance I attribute largely to the state college in town with its 9,000 students. Like sailors of old, there's plenty of weekend drunks willing to pull up a sleeve at the Pink Armadillo tattoo parlor, which seems to do a brisk business during the school year. I peek in, but I'm not tempted.

I learned from a neighbor here in North Fort Myers, FL that there's a mobile tattoo parlor operating in our unincorporated town. That's right—a truck much like a food truck—that pulls up in a shopping plaza parking lot for the day to ply the body art trade. Who'd have thunk it?! Still: I'm not tempted. But…

…I did end up with a tattoo after all in late 2022. A *temporary* tattoo! A half-inch sized Romanesque capital *V*. Quite discreet and stylish.

My Numero Uno lover mailed it to me in advance of our December rendezvous, asking that I sport it for him with explicit instructions on where to place it. So, once ensconced in my hotel suite I opened the Inbox.Com package and proceeded to follow the instructions to 1.

Prep skin with Primer Wipe, 2. Apply tattoo, and 3. Leave on for 60 minutes. Easy-peasy.

The smile on Uno's face upon seeing it? That smile will last a lifetime. And I'd do it again in a heartbeat. So, I'll do my temp tats from time to time, and I'll continue to photograph and admire others' body art, but as for me, the real thing? No. Never. My birthmark will suffice, thank you very much.

I love
the
stupid shit
that people
get
tattooed
when they're
smashed
in Zante.

Maisie Brown
I thought I was enlightened and other stories

When I was eighteen I thought I had reached enlightenment. More like *enwhitenment*. I really thought I was a proper arhat because I did a bit of meditation, liked to light incense and read the Penguin Classics 99p *Dhammapada*. Like I said, "enwhitened".

And so, for my first tattoo when I was eighteen of course I got a tattoo of a unalome… on my hand. I thought a hand tattoo just looked cool but had not considered that I was telling the world: "Hey, don't employ me. I'm only eighteen but if I only have tattoo space left on my hand, I must be covered!"

It never stopped me – though I can't say for sure – achieving my goals. I still scraped through university; I even managed to land a job in a law firm. But as a now-moderately-tattooed person myself, I do wonder what I was thinking.

Religion isn't really my thing anymore but I do not regret the unalome; it has held well and fits the hand nicely. But more than that, I have made peace with the person I was then, and to cover that up would make me feel I was denying my own growth.

During university I think I was still under the impression that tattoos had to have a backstory, and as a student of archaeology I was foaming at the mouth to have an Altai Princess tattoo. She was another permafrost body with a permafrost bodysuit, just so ye know.

I do *like* this tattoo, it is great, but it makes me cringe to explain. Not because of the slightly stuffy subject matter, but because I didn't really like my course that much. I barely even passed. So although it is a good tattoo, overall I find it hard to talk about.

The world of tattoos is a strange and personal one.

Getting tattooed is the epitome of bodily autonomy, and self-love, even self-care in many cases. Self-harm scars you fancy covering? Bam, tattoo, over. Self-conscious of your tummy? Tattoo on that tum, give yourself a reason to love it. Finally, medical tattoos provide vital insights into conditions and can save a person's life in emergency situations.

I feel privileged to be able to wear my tattoos. As a white woman in the UK I don't feel that being tattooed has affected my capacity to live and work.

Horitomo is an artist fighting for legitimacy in a country already steeped in tattoo history. The Japanese Irezumi tattoos of the past were status symbols, beautiful and intricate pieces designed to convey wealth; jewellery sans jewels or metals in a time when such ostentatious displays were forbidden.

However, during that time tattoos were also an established mark for criminals, who were essentially branded for their crimes. Even those who could afford large coverups were in essence isolating themselves further.

Horitomo is an artist of today still fighting to restore legitimacy to tattooing in Japan by combining Tebori – the tradition of hand poking using bamboo and needle or similar device – and Monmon, meaning *tattoo*.

His designs are a charming mix of his two loves: cats and tattooing. I feel anyone would be hard-pressed to look at his designs and feel a criminal connection. Not only is Horitomo's work helping to lessen the tattoo stigma in Japan but he has created a portfolio and *legacy* so iconic that I would argue it is already a part of our modern tattoo history.

So many places have kept their tattooing traditions alive. I think of Whang-Od Oggay of Buscalan, Tinglayan, Kalinga, Philippines. Though she no longer tattoos, the traditional Kalinga method has been passed down to her granddaughters. This is culture preserving itself without having to be stuffed, stamped and shipped to live forever behind a glass case and stared at by white people.

On a personal level, even those tattoos that aren't ground-breaking are so valid. I love the stupid shit that people get tattooed when they're smashed in Zante. If that's you, I love you. Wouldn't want to be you, but boy do I like looking at you.

Do you have a tattoo of a local kebab shop's logo in order to cop those lifelong free kebabs? Fucking more power to you friend.

A tattooed body will be with you forever, a selection of timeless images that may be deeply personal, deeply hilarious, well done, terribly done and anywhere in between. It is bodily autonomy at its finest. It is high art, low art, all at once. It is criminal; it is ancestral; it is old and new and changing and traditional. How beautiful and how freeing it is to be able to curate your own exhibition!

I asked Julian Bishop if he would share some background on his poem, Lobster. Here's what he wrote:

"I was working as a business journalist for the BBC and I'd hot-foot it down from White City to Holborn for my weekly poetry class. In this particular session we were studying prose poems and the challenge was to write one ourselves. I'd been watching pictures (or feeds, as we call them) come into the BBC from all over the world and one sequence particularly caught my eye – a lobster caught off the US coast with a Pepsi logo on its claw. The poor creature had clearly been lying on a pile of junk chucked into the ocean."

Julian Bishop
Lobster

Pepsi - it was the brand he grew up with - the sweet memory of it, the familiar tang of aluminium. Each night cradled in a cot of cans, suckled on bottles, sleeping on a seabed littered with plastic toys, tops spinning on the floor. Every one of them Pepsi. He dressed up in armour - it became a habit (with a Pepsi logo) - hung out with a pile of drifters, washed up types who didn't even look fine on the surface. They all drank Pepsi. He got a tattoo - festooned in red and blue, he soon became a brand ambassador, the extravagant fandangle spangled on a hand. But he threw it all away. Bottled it. Abandoned, he washed up on a beach - that's where I found him. Junked, with only a Pepsi filigree. Even his mother had sent him packing.

The end.

Thank you for reading.
We hope you enjoyed it. If so, please kindly consider
writing a short review on Amazon or Goodreads,
or tell a friend about this book,
or send us an email and tell us what you thought
and we'll share it on our website.

xx Guts

Our Contributors

Claire Askew's books include the creative writing guide *Novelista* (John Murray, 2020); the multi- award-winning novel *All The Hidden Truths* (Hodder, 2018) and the poetry collection *How To Burn A Woman* (Bloodaxe, 2021), which was the 2022 Saltire Scottish Poetry Book of the Year. Claire lives in Cumbria with her black cat, Winifred Sanderson.

Julian Bishop's first collection of eco poems called *We Saw It All Happen* was published earlier this year by Fly On The Wall Press. The book asks whether bearing witness to the climate emergency is enough or whether it's an excuse for disclaiming responsibility. A former environment journalist turned poet, he lives in Barnet with his family and dog and runs a small media company. He's worked for many years as both reporter and producer with the BBC and also on ITV's News At Ten. Contact: twitter @julianbpoet

Valerie Bence completed a PhD in her late-fifties and a Poetry MA in 2018. Rembrandt is her muse and the subject of her first collection *Falling in Love with a Dead Man* — published by Cinnamon Press (2019) following a year's mentoring. He is with her everyday, in the form of a tattoo. Overlap, her second pamphlet, was published in 2022 by the Emma Press.

Harriet Bradshaw is a journalist and camerawoman, known for reporting on climate change and filming on the frontline of the Coronavirus pandemic. She started writing short fiction for her mental well-being, having lost her friend and grandad during lockdown. She's currently finalising a novel, hoping to be professionally published one day.

Maisie Brown is a hobbyist who thinks everything is interesting. Queer, sincere and wielding a degree in

Archaeology and Anthropology. Composing articles, poems and stories on a range of topics: from nature to mythology; politics to pop culture; working-class history to video games; Maisie sees the sublime and the ridiculous in everything.

Meredith MacLeod Davidson is a poet and writer from Virginia. A graduate of Clemson University with a degree in English, her work has been published in The Bookends Review and elsewhere. Meredith serves in editorial roles for multiple literary journals, and is currently pursuing an MLitt in Creative Writing at the University of Glasgow.

Daniela Esposito is studying Screenwriting in Prague. She has been published in The Pomegranate London, Mono, Tears in the Fence, Bandit Fiction, the Templeman Review, Dream Noir, Writer's Block magazine and soon to be in Litro (US) and The Stand. She has been long-listed for the Bridport Prize and Brick Lane Short Story Prize.

Callum Henderson is a 30-year-old writer currently living in London. An author from a young age, he followed his prevailing passion to study Creative Writing and Journalism at the University of Strathclyde in Glasgow. In 2010, he was one of the winners of the Scottish Book Trust's coveted 'Young Writers Award.' He has previously been published in their collection *New Writing*, as well as in One Magazine (2011), the literary journal Quotidian (2016), and the anthology *If Only You Could See Yourself (And Other Stories)* (2012).

Liam Hogan is an award-winning short story writer, with stories in *Best of British Science Fiction* and in *Best of British Fantasy* (NewCon Press). He's been published by Analog, Daily Science Fiction, and Flame Tree Press, among others. He helps host Liars' League London, volunteers at the creative writing charity Ministry of Stories, and lives and avoids work in London. More details   at http://happyendingnotguaranteed.blogspot.co.uk

Erin Hosfield has been a tattooist in the city of Pittsburgh for nearly two decades. She has a BA in Fine Art from California University and she is a painter, writer, plant enthusiast, and Diet Coke addict. When she's not tattooing, she can be found in her garden, hunched over her keyboard, wrangling her sassy dogs, and creating far too many playlists.

Maria Jastrzębska is a poet, editor and translator who came to the UK from Poland as a child. Her most recent book is *Small Odysseys* (Waterloo Press 2022). She co-edited *Queer in Brighton* anthology (New Writing South 2014). Her work is translated into Polish and Romanian. She was writer for ACE-awarded cross-arts project Snow Q. www.mariajastrzebska.wordpress.com

Di Lebowitz is a heavily tattooed woman and feminist from Hong Kong with a Hong Kongese mother and Ashkenazi Jewish father, raised by her maternal grandmother. She is a survivor of sexual assault and author of her debut memoir *The Marks Left On Her*. She is also a Krav Maga Self Defense Instructor based in London.

Dominic Lyne is a London based writer. Drawing from his personal experiences, his works of transgressive fiction aim to shine a light upon the darker sides of humanity and society. He has been published by Rebel Satori Press and HarperCollins, and is a frequent contributor to SCAB Magazine.

Louisa Mastromarino is a certified counselor educator. She holds a Bachelor of Arts in Communications, a Master of Science in School Counseling, and a post master's degree in Supervision and Educational Leadership. Louisa is the author of several children's books including *Spifford Max and the Cycle Pups Go to Washington, D.C.*, *Spifford Max and the Cycle Pups Go to New York City*, *Spifford Max and the Cycle Pups Go to Philadelphia, Pennsylvania*, and *Brizzley Bear Loves Poetry*. www.LouisaMastro.com

Karla Linn Merrifield has 16 books to her credit. Her newest poetry collection, *My Body the Guitar*, was nominated for the 2022 National Book Award. She is a frequent contributor to The Songs of Eretz Poetry Review. Her website is: www.karlalinnmerrifield.org and her blog is: karlalinnmerrifeld.wordpress.com

Michał Kamil Piotrowski is a visual poet, text artist, and curator living and working in Folkestone, UK. He mostly writes experimental, visual, and technology-powered poetry. He enjoys making poetry interactive and he often works with found text. The themes he explores the most are technology, politics, love, and mental illnesses. His interactive book *The Cursory Remix* (2021, Contraband Books) has been co-written by Google Translate. IG: @somecoolwords

Emily Ricard was born in Geneva, Switzerland in 1993 to French/British parents. Following her move to London in 2009, she was able to develop her creative interests academically and personally, which include museums, photography and writing. When Emily isn't working on her debut novel, she enjoys travelling, volunteering with local charities, making Nutella crêpes and collecting taxidermy. She lives in London with her English bulldog Bianca.

Liz Beth Turner retrained as a therapist in 2017 and established a small mental health CIC on Anglesey where she lives with her husband, two rescue cats and a dog. She started penning poetry as therapy during serious illness in 2021 and now has established poetry therapy workshops.

She writes about social injustice, human suffering and mental health inspired by existentialism, science and art.

Sabrina Wolfe (she/her) is a writer who lives in London. She has worked as a journalist/editor for many years and been published in Time Out, The Simple Things and The Times, among others. Recently trained in garden design and horticulture, Sabrina can mostly be found writing at her desk, planting bulbs outside, or planning her next tattoo. 'Skin Deep' is her first piece of fiction to be published and she is currently writing a novel.

Copyrights for Individual Titles

About the Cover Art Photographer

 My name is Jayson Hinrichsen. I am a professional portrait/lifestyle photographer from Sioux City, Iowa. I started my photography career six years ago and never looked back. When I was in college I played baseball until I became sick and was diagnosed with ulcerative colitis which ended my baseball career early. I had a friend in my communications class ask me if I could shoot a music video for him and I said yes. That was the best decision I've ever made. After holding the camera I felt something special. That summer I bought my first camera and the rest is history. Photography has given me the opportunity to travel the world, shoot for celebrities, and reach millions of people. My goal is to inspire others and show people that anything is possible if you put your mind to it. No dream is too big.

Instagram: @rawe.reality

About Guts Publishing

Established in May 2019, we are an independent publisher in London. The name came from the obvious—it takes guts to publish just about anything. We are the home to the freaks and misfits of the literary world.

We like uncomfortable topics. Our tagline: Ballsy books about life. Our thinking: The book market has enough ball-less books and we're happy to shake things up a bit.

The Transformative Power of Tattoo (Sept 2023) is our ninth book.

Dear Mr Andrews (Jan 2023) by Lotte Latham is the true story of a young British woman's journey through the precarious landscape of sugar dating.

The Peanut Factory (May 2022) by Deborah Price is our coming-of-age 70s punk squatter memoir set in South London.

Blade in the Shadow (Oct 2021) by Jillian Halket is a coming-of-age memoir about a young Scottish woman struggling with undiagnosed obsessive compulsive disorder.

Fish Town (Apr 2021) by John Gerard Fagan is a young man's bittersweet departure from Glasgow and the next seven years of his life in a remote fishing village in Japan.

Sending Nudes (Jan 2021) is a collection of fiction, nonfiction and poetry about the various reasons people send nudes.

Euphoric Recall (Oct 2020) by Aidan Martin is the true story of a Scottish working-class lad and his recovery from addiction and trauma.

Cyber Smut (Sept 2020) is a collection of fiction, nonfiction and poetry about the effects of technology on our lives, our sexuality and how we love.

Stories About Penises (Nov 2019) is a collection of fiction, nonfiction and poetry about, well, exactly what it sounds like. To quote a prominent Australian author, 'Quite possibly the best title of the year.' We think so too.

Our website: gutspublishing.com
Our email: gutspublishing@gmail.com

Thank you for reading and thank you for your support!

Printed in Great Britain
by Amazon

ى0098